Hypercube Sudoku

Sudoku in Four Dimensions

By John Cooper

R I Publications

First published 2007 by R. I. Publications
13 Lambeecher, Bath Road, Balbriggan,
Co. Dublin, Ireland.
Tel +353 1 690 3395
E-mail: info@cooperpuzzles.com

ISBN: 978-0-9557713-0-9

Text and puzzles © John Cooper
Rules for Hypercube Sudoku © John Cooper
Design and Illustrations © John Cooper

Preface

The rules of Sudoku are incomplete! Besides the three standard rules, there are three other rules that complete the set. As the Sudoku grid is a representation of a 3 x 3 x 3 x 3 hypercube, the rules can be generalized into one rule: every (orthogonal) plane of the hypercube must contain each of nine symbols.

This book explores the meaning and ramifications of this rule and offers many testing challenges that this rule presents. Here's a Hypercube Sudoku puzzle below but you must use the rules for Hypercube Sudoku to solve this grid. Can you figure it out?

We will solve this step-by-step later in the book in chapter 3. But give it a try now if you think you understand hypercubes.

9							3	
			4		9		6	
		6						
6				3			4	
	1							8
	9			5			8	
							2	

Contents

1	Introduction	1
2	Rules	3
3	Let's Try One	7
4	Easier Puzzles	23
5	What Are the Four Dimension of Sudoku?	35
6	Medium Puzzles	53
7	Picture of a 4-D Rotation	67
8	Hard Puzzles	73
9	The Seventh Rule of Hypercube Sudoku	87
10	Very Hard Puzzles	97
11	Solutions	107

1. Introduction

As the Sudoku puzzle increases in popularity other versions emerge. Some of these change the shape of the blocks or the grid. Some add further restrictions on the allowed numbers. The possible permutations of the rules are boundless. This diversity of puzzle types boosts interest and complexity for those who like a logical challenge.

This book introduces a new set of rules that follows naturally from the structure of the puzzle. The Sudoku grid is a representation of a 3 x 3 x 3 x 3 4-dimensional hypercube. This leads logically to additional rules and gives an opportunity to explore 4-dimensional space.

The rules for Hypercube Sudoku can be stated that every (orthogonal) plane of the hypercube must contain each of nine symbols. Interpreting the ramifications of this rule is a puzzle in itself that some puzzle solvers might like to investigate. Those puzzlers might like to go directly to the puzzle pages and skip the specification and derivation of the new rules. The rules for Hypercube Sudoku include the rules for normal Sudoku and generalize and extend the standard rules.

The difficulty of puzzles with these hypercube rules varies depending on the initial clues, but the complexity can rival the most difficult puzzles of the standard version. One new type of challenge is in applying the new rules as the geometry is more complicated than columns, rows and blocks. The new rules also lead to types of logic that do not occur with the traditional version.

With more rules, more deductions can be construed from the clues. This means that fewer initial clues are needed to completely solve the grid. It is possible to solve some puzzles with only eight initial numbers.

I hope you enjoy these puzzles.

2. Hypercube Sudoku Rules

The game of Hypercube Sudoku can be played with just a few simple additions to the standard Sudoku game. In chapter 5 there is a discussion of the derivation of the rules for Hypercube Sudoku.

These rules are summarized here so that you can start solving puzzles quickly. The rules can be stated in terms of planes in hypercubes or coordinates, but they are more easily understood by the descriptions and diagrams below. Later you may like consider the source of these rules, the different ways to state them and how they apply to 4-dimensional space. These will be covered in later chapters, chapters 5 and 7.

The first three rules of Hypercube Sudoku are the same as standard Sudoku. In the Sudoku grid every row, column and 3 x 3 block must contain each of nine symbols (usually numbers 1 to 9). These are illustrated in the grids on the next page. The nine squares marked by X must contain nine different numbers. Also the nine squares marked by cross-hatching contain the nine different numbers, and the nine squares marked by dots contain the nine different numbers. These are just examples. There are nine sets of squares that follow each of these three rules.

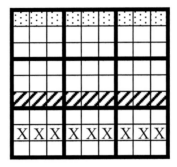

Row Rule

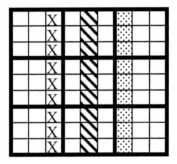

Column Rule

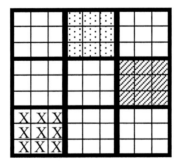

Block Rule

4

There are three additional rules for Hypercube Sudoku. These rules are perhaps best described in the diagrams on the next page as it is difficult to state them clearly in words. The diagrams show only three examples of the nine sets of nine cells which must contain each of the nine numbers.

Fourth rule of Hypercube Sudoku, Columns of Cells in Rows of Blocks:
In each row of blocks the columns of cells in the same relative position must contain each of the nine numbers.

Fifth rule of Hypercube Sudoku, Rows of Cells in Columns of Blocks:
In each column of blocks the rows of cells in the same relative position must contain each of the nine numbers.

Sixth rule of Hypercube Sudoku, Position of Cells within Blocks Rule:
All nine cells in the same relative position within the nine blocks must contain each of the nine numbers.

These rules are not arbitrary, but rather they complete and generalize the standard rules of Sudoku. The diagrams from the previous page are included here so that all the rules can be seen together.

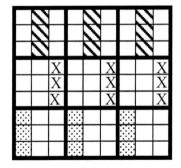

Columns of Cells in
Rows of Blocks Rule

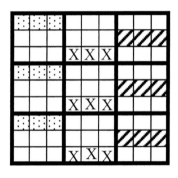

Rows of Cells in
Columns of Blocks
Rule

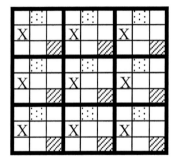

Position of Cells
within Blocks Rule

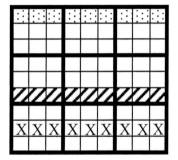

Row Rule

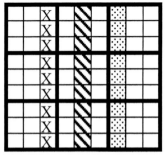

Column Rule

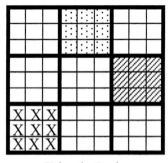

Block Rule

6

3. Let's Try One

Let's try a puzzle to get an idea of how these rules work. Here's a puzzle we can try together.

There are three 9's so let's start with them.

9							3	
			4		9		6	
		6						
6				3			4	
	1							8
	9			5			8	
							2	

In the upper right block 9 cannot be in the upper row or the middle row because there are 9's already in those rows, the Row Rule. The 9's in the other two top blocks are in the left and right columns. So the 9 in the upper right block cannot be in the right or left column, the Columns of Cells in a Row of Blocks Rule. This leaves only the bottom middle cell of this block for the 9.

The left middle block doesn't have a 9. It cannot be in the left or middle columns due to the Column Rule. The 9 in this block cannot be in the top or middle row due to the Rows of Cells in a Column of Blocks Rule. This just leaves the lower right cell for the 9 in the left middle block.

The grid now looks like this.

9							3	
			4		9		6	
		6					9	
6				3			4	
	1	9						8
	9			5			8	
							2	

It is now possible to determine the position of the 9 in the right middle block. Due to the 9 in the left middle block, the 9 in the right middle block cannot be in the bottom row, Row Rule, or in the right column, Column of Cells Rule. The 9 in this block cannot be in the upper middle cell due to the 9 right above it, Column Rule. The 9 cannot be in the upper left cell due to the 9 in the upper right cell in the upper right block, Position of

8

Cells Rule. This leaves only the left middle cell for the 9 in the right middle block.

The 9 can now be located in the very center block. Again the 9 in the left middle block eliminates the 9 from the bottom row, Row Rule, or in the right column, Column of Cells Rule. The 9 in the upper middle block is in the middle row so the 9 in the very center block cannot be in the middle row, Row of Cells Rule. Finally the 9 cannot be in the upper left cell due to the 9 in the upper left cell in the upper left block, Position of Cells Rule. This leaves only the upper middle cell for the 9 in the center block.

Similarly the 9's can be located for the other two blocks.
Can you find the reason for the 9's in the final two blocks?

9							3	
			4		9	6		
		6				*9*		
			9					
6			3			*9*	4	
	1	*9*						8
								9
	9		5			8		
			9			2		

There are also three 6's. That is a good place to look next. The 6's in the left top block and the left middle block eliminate two columns and two rows in the bottom left block. This leaves just one cell in this block in the top middle cell.

In the top row of blocks there are 6's in the bottom two rows and the 6's are in the middle and right columns. For the top middle block the 6 must go in the top left cell.

We can also determine the place for the 6 in the right middle block. The 6 in the left middle block rules out cells in the middle row and the left column. The 6 in the right top block rules out cells in the middle column. In the right middle block the lower right cell is already occupied. This leaves only the top right cell for the 6 in the right middle block.

9			6				3	
			4		9		6	
		6					9	
				9				6
6				3		9	4	
	1	9						8
	6							9
	9			5			8	
			9				2	

We can similarly find the location of the 6's in the final three blocks as shown below.

9			6				3	
			4		9	6		
		6				9		
			9					6
6			3			9	4	
	1	9	6					8
	6							9
	9		5	6		8		
			9			6	2	

Let's consider the 8's next. In the middle row of cells in the middle row of blocks, four cells are already occupied. The 8 in the right middle block rules out the cells in the right columns. The 8 in the right lower block is in the center cell. This rules out the center cell in the left middle block. All the cells in the middle row have 8 excluded from all the cells except the left middle cell in the center block.

Less complicated logic place an 8 in the upper left cell of the upper right block. The placement of the rest of the 8's can now be determined easily.

9			*6*			*8*	3	
		8	4		9		6	
		6		*8*			*9*	
	8			*9*				*6*
6			*8*	3		*9*	4	
	1	*9*		*6*				8
	6				*8*			*9*
	9			5	*6*		8	
8			*9*			*6*	2	

Let's look at the 3's now.

The two initial 3's exclude all the cells in the right middle block except the lower left cell. With this 3 we can easily find the location of the 3 in the lower right block and the left middle block. In the lower right block the 3 must be in the right column and it cannot be in the top or bottom row of the block.

9			6			8	3	
		8	4		9		6	
		6		8			9	
	8	3		9				6
6			8	3		9	4	
	1	9		6		3		8
	6				8			9
	9		5	6			8	3
8			9			6	2	

Now we can find the 3's in the top and bottom blocks in the middle. In the top middle block the 3 cannot be in the top row or middle row due to the 3's in the top right block and center block. Also the 3 cannot be in the lower left square due to the 3 in the right middle block. This leaves only the lower right square. In the lower middle block the 3 cannot be in the middle row or column due to the 3 in the block above. It cannot be in the right column because of the 3 in the right lower block. This leaves only the top left cell. Now we can easily locate the 3's in the final two blocks.

9			6			8	3	
3		8	4		9		6	
		6		8	3		9	
	8	3		9				6
6			8	3		9	4	
	1	9		6		3		8
	6		3		8			9
	9			5	6		8	3
8	3		9			6	2	

The 1 in the left middle block rules out all the unoccupied cells in the left top block except the top right cell. These two 1's determine the location of the 1 in the left lower block. These three 1's exclude all unoccupied squares in the second row from the top except the center square in the top middle block.

9		1	6			8	3	
3		8	4	1	9		6	
		6		8	3		9	
	8	3		9				6
6			8	3		9	4	
	1	9		6		3		8
	6		3		8			9
1	9			5	6		8	3
8	3		9			6	2	

The locations of the rest of the 1's become known one-by-one starting with the lower middle block and then the center block.

9		1	6			8	3	
3		8	4	1	9		6	
		6		8	3		9	
	8	3	1	9				6
6			8	3		9	4	
	1	9		6		3		8
	6		3		8			9
1	9			5	6		8	3
8	3		9		1	6	2	

Of the blocks on the right the 1 in the middle is easiest to locate and the other two follow.

9		1	6			8	3	
3		8	4	1	9		6	
		6		8	3	1	9	
	8	3	1	9				6
6			8	3		9	4	1
	1	9		6		3		8
	6		3		8		1	9
1	9			5	6		8	3
8	3		9		1	6	2	

Let's look at the 2's next.

With so many cells occupied it is easy to see where the 2's go in the right middle block and bottom middle block.

9		1	6			8	3	
3		8	4	1	9		6	
		6		8	3	1	9	
	8	3	1	9		2		6
6			8	3		9	4	1
	1	9		6		3		8
	6		3		8		1	9
1	9		2	5	6		8	3
8	3		9		1	6	2	

Now we easily see where to put the 2's in the lower left, upper right and center blocks.

9		1	6			8	3	
3		8	4	1	9		6	2
		6		8	3	1	9	
	8	3	1	9		2		6
6			8	3		9	4	1
	1	9		6	2	3		8
	6	2	3		8		1	9
1	9		2	5	6		8	3
8	3		9		1	6	2	

The location of the 2's in the final three blocks follow directly.

9		1	6	2		8	3	
3		8	4	1	9		6	2
2		6		8	3	1	9	
	8	3	1	9		2		6
6	2		8	3		9	4	1
	1	9		6	2	3		8
	6	2	3		8		1	9
1	9		2	5	6		8	3
8	3		9		1	6	2	

Now some of the rows and blocks are nearly complete. We can look for which numbers can complete them. The row second from the bottom has every number except 4 and 7. In the lower right block 4 cannot go in the left middle cell as 4 is in the middle row in the block above. So 7 goes in this cell and 4 goes in the other vacant cell in that row.

The row second from the top is also missing only two numbers, 5 and 7. There is a 5 in the center cell of the lower middle block so 5 cannot go in the center cell of the upper left block. A 7 must go there and the 5 goes in the other empty cell of this row.

18

Also the very middle row is missing only two numbers, 5 and 7. The 5 in the bottom middle block excludes a 5 from going into the middle row of the center block. So 7 goes in the empty cell in the middle row of the center block and 5 goes in the other empty cell in this row.

The grid now looks like this.

9		1	6	2		8	3	
3	7	8	4	1	9	5	6	2
2		6		8	3	1	9	
	8	3	1	9		2		6
6	2	5	8	3	7	9	4	1
	1	9		6	2	3		8
	6	2	3		8		1	9
1	9	4	2	5	6	7	8	3
8	3		9		1	6	2	

With so many cells filled in it is easy to complete the grid starting with the center, upper middle and lower right blocks.

With these three blocks completed the grid looks like this.

9		1	6	2	5	8	3	
3	7	8	4	1	9	5	6	2
2		6	7	8	3	1	9	
	8	3	1	9	4	2		6
6	2	5	8	3	7	9	4	1
	1	9	5	6	2	3		8
	6	2	3		8	4	1	9
1	9	4	2	5	6	7	8	3
8	3		9		1	6	2	5

Here is the completed grid.

9	4	1	6	2	5	8	3	7
3	7	8	4	1	9	5	6	2
2	5	6	7	8	3	1	9	4
7	8	3	1	9	4	2	5	6
6	2	5	8	3	7	9	4	1
4	1	9	5	6	2	3	7	8
5	6	2	3	7	8	4	1	9
1	9	4	2	5	6	7	8	3
8	3	7	9	4	1	6	2	5

Notice that every number is in every row, every column, and every block and also in every corresponding row in a column of blocks and every corresponding column in every row of blocks and every corresponding position among all the blocks.

Of course at many stages in this solution one could go in a different course to solve the puzzle. The cells could be filled in a different order. The purpose of this discussion is to show a way that the new rules of Hypercube Sudoku can be used to solve a grid. Furthermore, please notice that this puzzle can not be solved by standard Sudoku rules. There are not enough spaces filled initially. At some point after enough spaces are filled the solution can be completed with only the standard rules.

Standard Sudoku puzzles usually start with 22 to 25 spaces filled. Hypercube Sudoku puzzles need only about 12 spaces filled to start. In some puzzles only eight spaces are filled initially. This is one reason Hypercube Sudoku is so challenging. Of course the more complicated geometry also makes Hypercube Sudoku challenging.

It is also interesting to note that all completed Hypercube Sudoku grids follow the standard Sudoku rules. This is because Hypercube Sudoku includes the standard Sudoku rules. Hypercube Sudoku rules are a generalization of standard Sudoku rules.

The reverse is not true. Most published standard Sudoku solutions do not follow the additional

Hypercube Sudoku rules. There is no need for standard Sudoku to follow Hypercube Sudoku rules. If one knew that a standard Sudoku puzzle also followed Hypercube Sudoku rules, the puzzle would be much easier to solve.

In the following chapter are several Hypercube Sudoku puzzles to solve. They will be mostly easier problems. Chapters with more complicated puzzles appear later in the book.

4. Some Easier Puzzles

I hope these aren't too hard.

	7						5	
		3						
			7					
			1					
		6			2			
4		2	8					
					1			
				4		5	8	

Puzzle **1** Easy

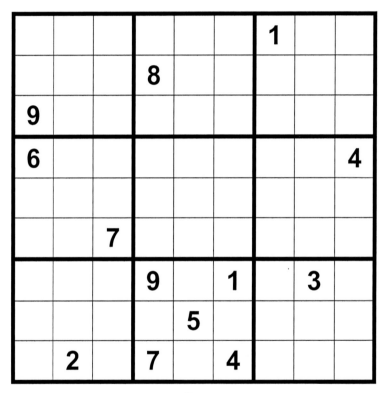

Puzzle **2** Easy

Hint: Where cannot the 2 go due to the Rows of Cells in a Column of Blocks Rule?

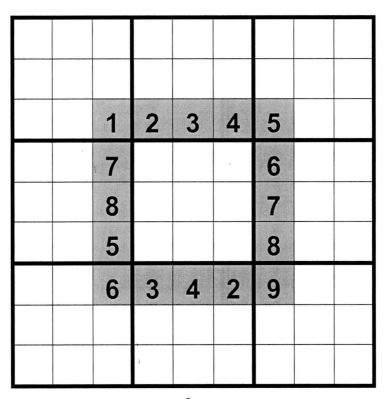

Puzzle **3** Easy

A Square Puzzle

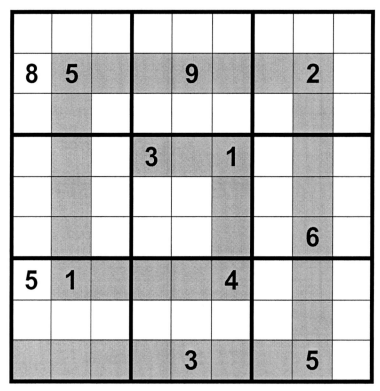

Puzzle **4** Easy

A Pi Spiral

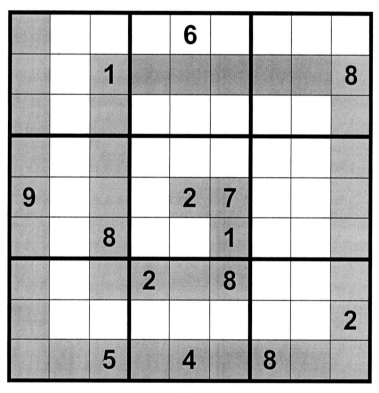

Puzzle **5** Easy

An e Spiral

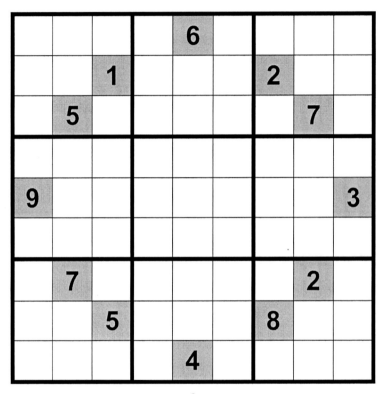

Puzzle **6** Easy

A Gem

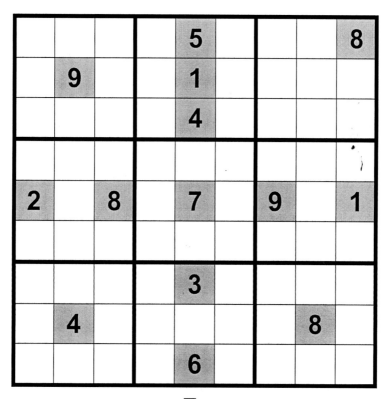

Puzzle **7** Easy

Crystal

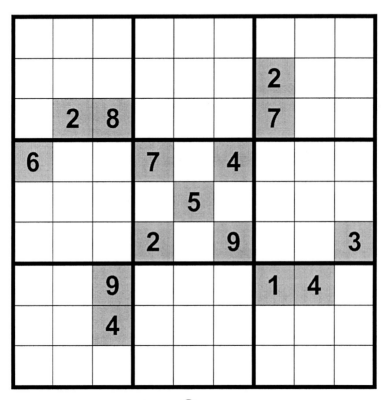

Puzzle **8** Easy

A Spiral Arm Galaxy

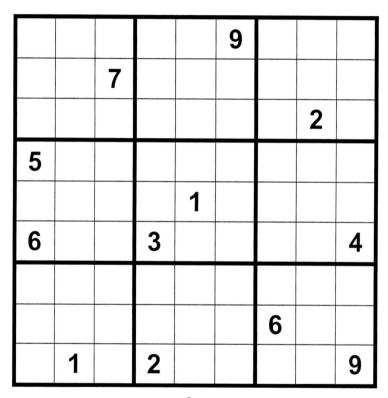

Puzzle **9** Easy

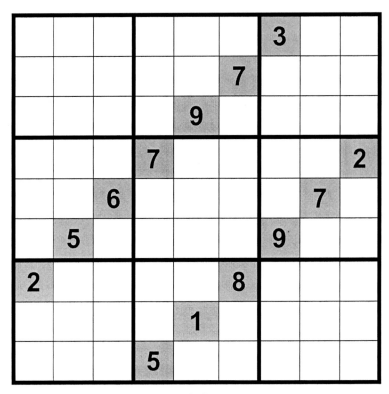

Puzzle **10** Easy

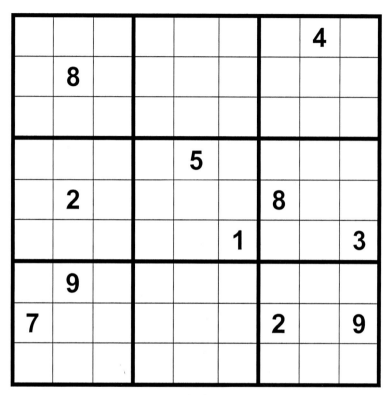

Puzzle **11** Easy

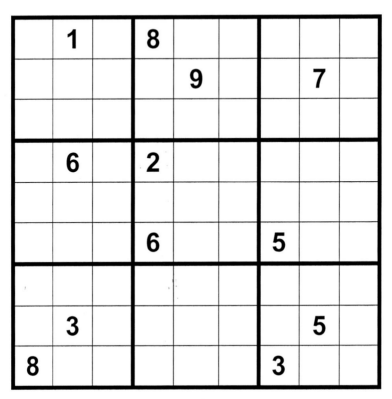

Puzzle **12** Easy

5. What Are The Four Dimensions Of Sudoku?

The Sudoku grid arrangement lends itself to four dimensional analyses. This can let us explore the mysterious world of hypercubes. Hypercubes are like squares or cubes except hypercubes have four dimensions. Squares have two dimensions, length and breadth. Cubes have three dimensions, length, breadth and height. Hypercubes have these three dimensions and a fourth dimension.

There are four features to the Sudoku cells; the horizontal and vertical placement of the block, and the horizontal and vertical placement of the cell within its block. These four features can be represented by four dimensions of a hypercube.

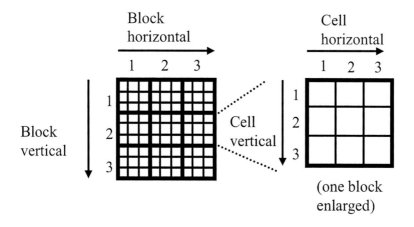

Before picturing these four dimensions, let's review how two and three dimensions are represented on paper.

A two dimensional graph as shown below has an x (horizontal) component and a y (vertical) component. The position of point A is described by two numbers, called coordinates, written inside brackets. For point A the coordinates are (3, 1). The arrowed lines are called axes. They originate from the zero point called the origin.

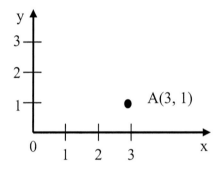

To represent a third dimension a third line is added at an angle at the origin as shown below. The three lines look like a corner of a room looks where two walls and the floor meet. Point B is 2 to the right, 3 up and 3 forward away from the back wall. This represents three dimensions on two-dimensional paper.

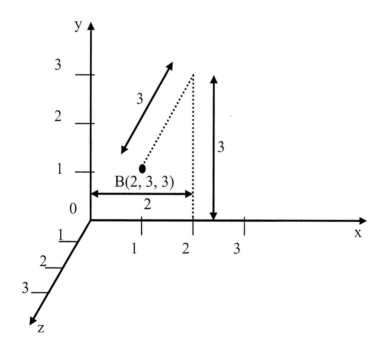

To represent four dimensions on two-dimensional paper, we draw several three-dimensional axes. The fourth dimension goes along the w-axis. The coordinate in the fourth dimension determines which of the three dimensional axes to plot the point. Point C has a w-coordinate of 2, so it is drawn on the second three-dimensional axis.

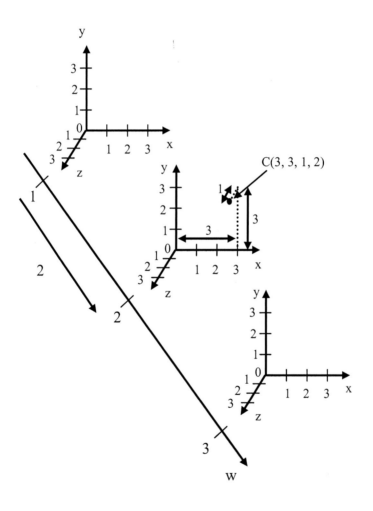

C(3, 3, 1, 2)

In the Sudoku grid below the squares are drawn as little cubes.

If the middle three columns are placed on the right three columns and then the left three columns are placed on top of all, there will be a 3 x 3 x 9 three-dimensional block as shown below on the left. Then separate the blocks as shown below on the right. There are three 3 x 3 x 3 cubes. This is the description of a 3 x 3 x 3 x 3 hypercube.

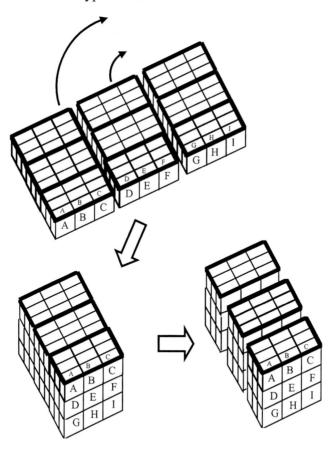

One rule in Sudoku is that every 3 x 3 block within the darker lines must contain each of the numbers from 1 to 9. These blocks are horizontal layers in the 3-D cubes in the hypercube. For instance, the lower left block in the Sudoku grid becomes the top layer of the front cube in the hypercube in the previous page.

Another rule in Sudoku is that every horizontal line in the grid must contain the nine different numbers. In the rearrangement on the previous page horizontal lines become vertical, forward-facing layers of the 3-D cubes of the hypercube. For instance, the row labelled A through I in the grid becomes the front vertical face in the hypercube.

The third and final rule in Sudoku is every column in the grid must contain the nine different numbers. (These rules are also rules in Hypercube Sudoku; call them the first three rules of Hypercube Sudoku.) In the hypercube a column becomes three columns of three cubes; the three columns are in the three different 3-D cubes and are each in the same relative position in the three different cubes.

A different rearrangement of the grid makes the columns of the grid into a layer of a cube. The rearrangement of the Sudoku grid on the previous page started by layering 3 x 9 rectangles. The rectangles are three cubes across and nine cubes deep. They are moved up and to the right. The Sudoku grid could also be arranged by rectangles nine across and three deep moving up and back on top of the layers to the rear as shown on the next page.

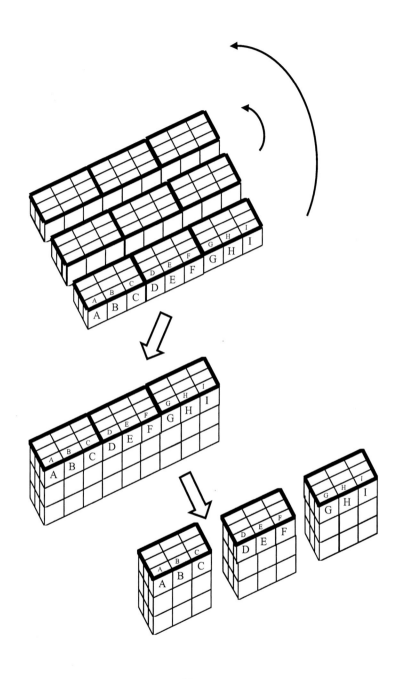

This rearrangement of the Sudoku grid also represents a hypercube. In this arrangement a column becomes a left/right facing vertical layer of a 3-D cube. For example, the column on the grid behind cube A would become the leftmost left-facing vertical layer.

Let's be clear now: these two arrangements are the same hypercube just seen from a different perspective. It is similar to rotating a square or cube. Rotating a cube does not make it a different cube; it just gives it a different orientation. Rearranging the small cubes BY CERTAIN RULES does not make a different hypercube; it just gives a different perspective.

New rules for Hypercube Sudoku: We see that the rules of Sudoku mean that certain layers of 3-D cubes of the hypercube must contain all nine numbers. Let's make a rule that all layers of the 3-D cubes must contain all nine numbers whether they are oriented up, forward or left/right. This would mean that in the cube with the letters A through I on the front face, the vertical face on the left would also have to contain all the nine numbers. There are eight other layers in this representation also facing left/right. They also must contain each of the nine numbers. Let's see how this translates back to the Sudoku grid.

The left facing layer in the 3-D cube in the diagram on page 39 would come from the squares marked with an 'X' in the grid below. Two other sets of nine squares are marked with cross hatching and dots. As with all the other rules, there are nine sets of squares that follow this rule. It can be stated as follows:

Fourth rule of Hypercube Sudoku, Columns of Cells in Rows of Blocks:
In each row of blocks the columns of cells in the same relative position must contain each of the nine numbers.

(This description is similar to the description of a column of squares in the hypercube shown above.)

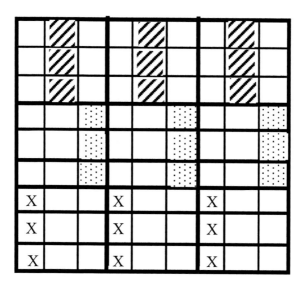

We also discussed a way of arranging the grid so that a column of squares would be on the left/right facing layer. This is shown on page 41. In a similar vein as the fourth rule and making all layers in the 3-D cubes contain all the nine numbers; the forward facing layers of this arrangement must contain each of the nine numbers. In the Sudoku grid some sets of squares that must contain all the nine numbers are shown below.

Fifth rule of Hypercube Sudoku, Rows of Cells in Columns of Blocks:
In each column of blocks the rows of cells in the same relative position must contain each of the nine numbers.

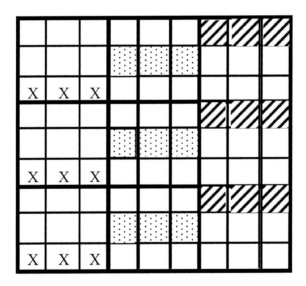

The sixth rule of Hypercube Sudoku

There are other ways to 'rotate ' a hypercube to 'see' different layers in 3-D cubes. These rotations delve deeply into the fourth dimension. Before demonstrating this graphically let's look at the coordinates of the sets of squares that must contain all nine numbers.

Let's call the horizontal position coordinate of a block, xb, and the vertical position coordinate of a block yb. Let's call the horizontal position coordinate of a cell within a block, xc, and the vertical position coordinate of a cell within a block yc. This is like the ordinary x and y coordinates and add b or c to it to denote block or cell. We write the coordinates of a cell as
(xb, yb, xc, yc). The first two coordinates specify the position of the block. The second two coordinates are the position of the cell within the block.

On the next page is a Sudoku grid with the coordinates displayed in each grid. Due to size considerations the four numbers are displayed on two lines. This display has the advantage that the block coordinates are separate from the cell coordinates. The block coordinates are on the top line and the cell coordinates are below. The coordinates progress from the lower left corner.

Let's look for patterns in the coordinates of cells that are grouped by the Sudoku rules.

The coordinates of the cells in the block in the first row and the first column are (1, 1, 1, 1), (1, 1, 1, 2), (1, 1, 1, 3), (1, 1, 2, 1), (1, 1, 2, 2), (1, 1, 2, 3), (1, 1, 3, 1), (1, 1, 3, 2), (1, 1, 3, 3). Notice the first two coordinates are all the same, (1, 1, ...). Of course, they are the coordinates of the same block. The coordinates in the other two positions cover all nine possibilities within the block. Those are the nine places that must contain each of the different nine numbers. A similar thing occurs with the nine cells in each of the other blocks; the block coordinates are the same and the cell coordinates cover the nine possibilities.

(1, 3, 1, 3)	(1, 3, 2, 3)	(1, 3, 3, 3)	(2, 3, 1, 3)	(2, 3, 2, 3)	(2, 3, 3, 3)	(3, 3, 1, 3)	(3, 3, 2, 3)	(3, 3, 3, 3)
(1, 3, 1, 2)	(1, 3, 2, 2)	(1, 3, 3, 2)	(2, 3, 1, 2)	(2, 3, 2, 2)	(2, 3, 3, 2)	(3, 3, 1, 2)	(3, 3, 2, 2)	(3, 3, 3, 2)
(1, 3, 1, 1)	(1, 3, 2, 1)	(1, 3, 3, 1)	(2, 3, 1, 1)	(2, 3, 2, 1)	(2, 3, 3, 1)	(3, 3, 1, 1)	(3, 3, 2, 1)	(3, 3, 3, 1)
(1, 2, 1, 3)	(1, 2, 2, 3)	(1, 2, 3, 3)	(2, 2, 1, 3)	(2, 2, 2, 3)	(2, 2, 3, 3)	(3, 2, 1, 3)	(3, 2, 2, 3)	(3, 2, 3, 3)
(1, 2, 1, 2)	(1, 2, 2, 2)	(1, 2, 3, 2)	(2, 2, 1, 2)	(2, 2, 2, 2)	(2, 2, 3, 2)	(3, 2, 1, 2)	(3, 2, 2, 2)	(3, 2, 3, 2)
(1, 2, 1, 1)	(1, 2, 2, 1)	(1, 2, 3, 1)	(2, 2, 1, 1)	(2, 2, 2, 1)	(2, 2, 3, 1)	(3, 2, 1, 1)	(3, 2, 2, 1)	(3, 2, 3, 1)
(1, 1, 1, 3)	(1, 1, 2, 3)	(1, 1, 3, 3)	(2, 1, 1, 3)	(2, 1, 2, 3)	(2, 1, 3, 3)	(3, 1, 1, 3)	(3, 1, 2, 3)	(3, 1, 3, 3)
(1, 1, 1, 2)	(1, 1, 2, 2)	(1, 1, 3, 2)	(2, 1, 1, 2)	(2, 1, 2, 2)	(2, 1, 3, 2)	(3, 1, 1, 2)	(3, 1, 2, 2)	(3, 1, 3, 2)
(1, 1, 1, 1)	(1, 1, 2, 1)	(1, 1, 3, 1)	(2, 1, 1, 1)	(2, 1, 2, 1)	(2, 1, 3, 1)	(3, 1, 1, 1)	(3, 1, 2, 1)	(3, 1, 3, 1)

Now consider the coordinates of the nine squares in the first row: (1, 1, 1, 1), (1, 1, 2, 1), (1, 1, 3, 1), (2, 1, 1, 1), (2, 1, 2, 1), (2, 1, 3, 1), (3, 1, 1, 1), (3, 1, 2, 1), (3, 1, 3, 1). In this case the coordinates that stay the same are in the 2nd and 4th positions, the yb and yc coordinates. In the diagram these are the second number in the top and bottom line in each cell. One is above the other. The xb and yb coordinates vary to cover the nine positions in the row.

It is the same case for any row of cells. the 2nd and 4th coordinates are the same. In the diagram these are the second number in the top line and the second number in the bottom line.

The coordinates in a column show a similar pattern. In a column the xb and the xc coordinates are all the same and the yb and yc coordinates vary. In the diagram these are the first number in the first line and the first number in the second line.

What about the fourth rule? The coordinates of the cells surrounded by the bold rectangles in the diagram on the next page are: (1, 1, 1, 1), (1, 1, 1, 2), (1, 1, 1, 3), (2, 1, 1, 1), (2, 1, 1, 2), (2, 1, 1, 3), (3, 1, 1, 1), (3, 1, 1, 2), (3, 1, 1, 3). Here the 2nd and 3rd coordinates remain the same, they are the y-coordinate of the block and the x-coordinate of the cell. In the diagram these two coordinates are on a diagonal line that angles down and to the left. Some examples are boxed in rectangles.

Similarly the 2nd and 3rd coordinates in the shaded cells are all (.., 3, 2, ..). These are also on a diagonal down and to the left.

It is the same case for every set of corresponding columns in a row of blocks. the coordinates on the diagonal from top right to bottom left, the 2nd and 3rd coordinates, are the same.

(1, 3, 1, 3)	(1, 3, 2, 3)	(1, 3, 3, 3)	(2, 3, 1, 3)	(2, 3, 2, 3)	(2, 3, 3, 3)	(3, 3, 1, 3)	(3, 3, 2, 3)	(3, 3, 3, 3)
(1, 3, 1, 2)	(1, 3, 2, 2)	(1, 3, 3, 2)	(2, 3, 1, 2)	(2, 3, 2, 2)	(2, 3, 3, 2)	(3, 3, 1, 2)	(3, 3, 2, 2)	(3, 3, 3, 2)
(1, 3, 1, 1)	(1, 3, 2, 1)	(1, 3, 3, 1)	(2, 3, 1, 1)	(2, 3, 2, 1)	(2, 3, 3, 1)	(3, 3, 1, 1)	(3, 3, 2, 1)	(3, 3, 3, 1)
(1, 2, 1, 3)	(1, 2, 2, 3)	(1, 2, 3, 3)	(2, 2, 1, 3)	(2, 2, 2, 3)	(2, 2, 3, 3)	(3, 2, 1, 3)	(3, 2, 2, 3)	(3, 2, 3, 3)
(1, 2, 1, 2)	(1, 2, 2, 2)	(1, 2, 3, 2)	(2, 2, 1, 2)	(2, 2, 2, 2)	(2, 2, 3, 2)	(3, 2, 1, 2)	(3, 2, 2, 2)	(3, 2, 3, 2)
(1, 2, 1, 1)	(1, 2, 2, 1)	(1, 2, 3, 1)	(2, 2, 1, 1)	(2, 2, 2, 1)	(2, 2, 3, 1)	(3, 2, 1, 1)	(3, 2, 2, 1)	(3, 2, 3, 1)
(1, 1, 1, 3)	(1, 1, 2, 3)	(1, 1, 3, 3)	(2, 1, 1, 3)	(2, 1, 2, 3)	(2, 1, 3, 3)	(3, 1, 1, 3)	(3, 1, 2, 3)	(3, 1, 3, 3)
(1, 1, 1, 2)	(1, 1, 2, 2)	(1, 1, 3, 2)	(2, 1, 1, 2)	(2, 1, 2, 2)	(2, 1, 3, 2)	(3, 1, 1, 2)	(3, 1, 2, 2)	(3, 1, 3, 2)
(1, 1, 1, 1)	(1, 1, 2, 1)	(1, 1, 3, 1)	(2, 1, 1, 1)	(2, 1, 2, 1)	(2, 1, 3, 1)	(3, 1, 1, 1)	(3, 1, 2, 1)	(3, 1, 3, 1)

With the fifth rule the x-coordinate of the block and the y coordinate of the cell remain the same while the other two coordinates vary to cover nine cells. We can see that in the diagram below.

In the shaded cells in the left column the coordinates on the diagonal from the top left to the bottom right are all 1, 3. These coordinates are marked by ovals. There is a similar case for all corresponding rows in a column of blocks. Another example is marked by slanting rectangles.

(1, 3, 1, 3)	(1, 3, 2, 3)	(1, 3, 3, 3)	(2, 3, 1, 3)	(2, 3, 2, 3)	(2, 3, 3, 3)	(3, 3, 1, 3)	(3, 3, 2, 3)	(3, 3, 3, 3)
(1, 3, 1, 2)	(1, 3, 2, 2)	(1, 3, 3, 2)	(2, 3, 1, 2)	(2, 3, 2, 2)	(2, 3, 3, 2)	(3, 3, 1, 2)	(3, 3, 2, 2)	(3, 3, 3, 2)
(1, 3, 1, 1)	(1, 3, 2, 1)	(1, 3, 3, 1)	(2, 3, 1, 1)	(2, 3, 2, 1)	(2, 3, 3, 1)	(3, 3, 1, 1)	(3, 3, 2, 1)	(3, 3, 3, 1)
(1, 2, 1, 3)	(1, 2, 2, 3)	(1, 2, 3, 3)	(2, 2, 1, 3)	(2, 2, 2, 3)	(2, 2, 3, 3)	(3, 2, 1, 3)	(3, 2, 2, 3)	(3, 2, 3, 3)
(1, 2, 1, 2)	(1, 2, 2, 2)	(1, 2, 3, 2)	(2, 2, 1, 2)	(2, 2, 2, 2)	(2, 2, 3, 2)	(3, 2, 1, 2)	(3, 2, 2, 2)	(3, 2, 3, 2)
(1, 2, 1, 1)	(1, 2, 2, 1)	(1, 2, 3, 1)	(2, 2, 1, 1)	(2, 2, 2, 1)	(2, 2, 3, 1)	(3, 2, 1, 1)	(3, 2, 2, 1)	(3, 2, 3, 1)
(1, 1, 1, 3)	(1, 1, 2, 3)	(1, 1, 3, 3)	(2, 1, 1, 3)	(2, 1, 2, 3)	(2, 1, 3, 3)	(3, 1, 1, 3)	(3, 1, 2, 3)	(3, 1, 3, 3)
(1, 1, 1, 2)	(1, 1, 2, 2)	(1, 1, 3, 2)	(2, 1, 1, 2)	(2, 1, 2, 2)	(2, 1, 3, 2)	(3, 1, 1, 2)	(3, 1, 2, 2)	(3, 1, 3, 2)
(1, 1, 1, 1)	(1, 1, 2, 1)	(1, 1, 3, 1)	(2, 1, 1, 1)	(2, 1, 2, 1)	(2, 1, 3, 1)	(3, 1, 1, 1)	(3, 1, 2, 1)	(3, 1, 3, 1)

With each rule a pair of coordinates remains the same while the other pair vary to describe nine squares that must contain the nine numbers. There are six ways to pair the four coordinates. So far there are rules covering five of these pairings. The sixth pairing are the xc and yc coordinates. This means for every position within the blocks there must be nine different numbers in that position in the nine different blocks.

Sixth rule of Hypercube Sudoku, Position of Cells within Blocks Rule:
All nine cells in the same relative position within the nine blocks must contain each of the nine numbers.

This can perhaps be better understood from the diagram below. The positions marked by an 'X' must contain all the nine numbers. These positions marked by an 'X' are all the lower left-hand position of the block. Similarly the cross-hatched and dotted squares show nine squares that must contain all of the nine numbers. The cross-hatched squares are all in the upper-middle position of their block. The dotted squares are all in the middle-right position of the block. Of course, there are six other sets of nine squares that must contain all nine numbers according to rule six.

In the grid of coordinates below we can see that cells in the same relative position in the block have the same 3rd and 4th coordinates. These are the two coordinates in the second line. For example the bottom left cells in each block have 1, 1 for their last two coordinates. These cells are marked by boxes and their like coordinates are encircled by ovals.

The xc, yc coordinates for the upper middle cells in each block are 2, 3. These cells are shaded and their like coordinates are surrounded by rectangles.

(1, 3, 1, 3)	(1, 3, 2, 3)	(1, 3, 3, 3)	(2, 3, 1, 3)	(2, 3, 2, 3)	(2, 3, 3, 3)	(3, 3, 1, 3)	(3, 3, 2, 3)	(3, 3, 3, 3)
(1, 3, 1, 2)	(1, 3, 2, 2)	(1, 3, 3, 2)	(2, 3, 1, 2)	(2, 3, 2, 2)	(2, 3, 3, 2)	(3, 3, 1, 2)	(3, 3, 2, 2)	(3, 3, 3, 2)
(1, 3, 1, 1)	(1, 3, 2, 1)	(1, 3, 3, 1)	(2, 3, 1, 1)	(2, 3, 2, 1)	(2, 3, 3, 1)	(3, 3, 1, 1)	(3, 3, 2, 1)	(3, 3, 3, 1)
(1, 2, 1, 3)	(1, 2, 2, 3)	(1, 2, 3, 3)	(2, 2, 1, 3)	(2, 2, 2, 3)	(2, 2, 3, 3)	(3, 2, 1, 3)	(3, 2, 2, 3)	(3, 2, 3, 3)
(1, 2, 1, 2)	(1, 2, 2, 2)	(1, 2, 3, 2)	(2, 2, 1, 2)	(2, 2, 2, 2)	(2, 2, 3, 2)	(3, 2, 1, 2)	(3, 2, 2, 2)	(3, 2, 3, 2)
(1, 2, 1, 1)	(1, 2, 2, 1)	(1, 2, 3, 1)	(2, 2, 1, 1)	(2, 2, 2, 1)	(2, 2, 3, 1)	(3, 2, 1, 1)	(3, 2, 2, 1)	(3, 2, 3, 1)
(1, 1, 1, 3)	(1, 1, 2, 3)	(1, 1, 3, 3)	(2, 1, 1, 3)	(2, 1, 2, 3)	(2, 1, 3, 3)	(3, 1, 1, 3)	(3, 1, 2, 3)	(3, 1, 3, 3)
(1, 1, 1, 2)	(1, 1, 2, 2)	(1, 1, 3, 2)	(2, 1, 1, 2)	(2, 1, 2, 2)	(2, 1, 3, 2)	(3, 1, 1, 2)	(3, 1, 2, 2)	(3, 1, 3, 2)
(1, 1, 1, 1)	(1, 1, 2, 1)	(1, 1, 3, 1)	(2, 1, 1, 1)	(2, 1, 2, 1)	(2, 1, 3, 1)	(3, 1, 1, 1)	(3, 1, 2, 1)	(3, 1, 3, 1)

This has been an explanation of the Sixth Rule of Hypercube Sudoku from the viewpoint of coordinates. This explanation is a bit easier to make and, perhaps, easier to understand than imagining these planes in four dimensions.

In chapter 7 we shall see how to 'rotate' a hypercube so that these squares in the same relative position in a block appear as layers in a cube of a hypercube.

4. Medium Puzzles

7							3	
			9		7			
		4						
4				3			9	
	8							6
	7			2			6	
							1	

Puzzle **13** Medium

					6		4	
	8		5					
				5				
	2					8		
					1			
	9							
7						2		9

Puzzle **14** Medium

9								
	6						2	
		2		5		7		
		4		8		9		
		6		3		1		
	1						7	

Puzzle **15** Medium

Puzzle **16** Medium

						2		
	5							
9					8			
			3					
6								
		4						
								1
				6				

Puzzle **17** Medium

1		7				5		
9			4			3		
	5	8						
					2			
3	6							

Puzzle **18** Medium

58

								8
						9	2	
					1			5
				5				
5			2					
	7	4						
3								

Puzzle **19** Medium

			8	7	5			
		9				8		
2	3						9	4
		8				6		
			7		8			

Puzzle **20** Medium

				4				9
							5	
			8	3				
			1					
		6						
		4	9					
	8							
7			2					

Puzzle **21** Medium

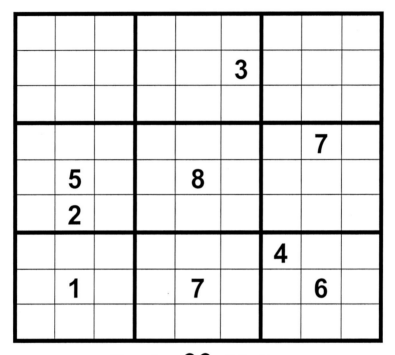

Puzzle **22** Medium

				3				
			4		1			
		8				4		
	7					9	8	
		5				7		
			1		6			
				9				

Puzzle **23** Medium

				2				
			1	5	7			
		5				6		
			3		9			
				9				
				4				

Puzzle **24** Medium

				7		8		
		6	9			4		
			8					
5						3		
								1

Puzzle **25** Medium

				3		2		
								8
	4	7			8			
		5						
1		4			6			

Puzzle **26** Medium

7. Picture of a 4-D Rotation

In chapter five we saw how a Sudoku grid could be stacked to make three cubes. We also saw how the faces and other layers could be used to describe the three original rules of Sudoku. The rows and columns of the Sudoku grid become faces and other layers of the cubes. Each of the layers must contain all nine numbers.

We also saw how stacking the Sudoku grid into three cubes leads to rules four and five of Hypercube Sudoku. The stacking produces other layers from a different orientation. Rules four and five state that these other layers must also contain each of the nine numbers. These conditions are not specified by the standard Sudoku rules.

The Hypercube Sudoku rules generalize the initial Sudoku rules so that every layer of the 4-D cube contains all nine numbers.

The sixth Rule of Hypercube Sudoku was not visually apparent in chapter five. Instead we derived the sixth rule by considering the four coordinates of the spaces in the hypercube. We noticed that in the first five rules each layer of the hypercube two coordinates remain the same while the other two coordinates varied to cover the nine spaces.

There are six ways to make pairs of the four coordinates of a hypercube. Five of these pairings correspond to the first five rules of Hypercube Sudoku.

The sixth pairing corresponds to grouping squares that have the same relative position in the blocks of the Sudoku grid.

The sixth rule of Hypercube Sudoku states that all squares in the same relative position in the blocks must also contain all the nine numbers. We made this rule by considering coordinates, not by showing them as being layers in the hypercube.

Here we shall stack, unstack and restack the layers until these squares appear as layers in the hypercube. This is equivalent to rotating a hypercube in four dimensions.

In chapter five we started by stacking columns of blocks on top of each other and then separating the stack to make three cubes.

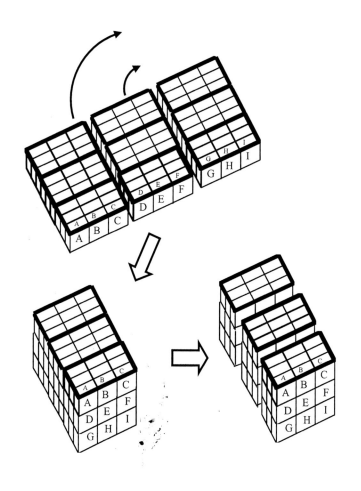

The next step is to stack the three cubes on top of each other. Notice this makes all the squares that were originally in the same relative position into a vertical column.

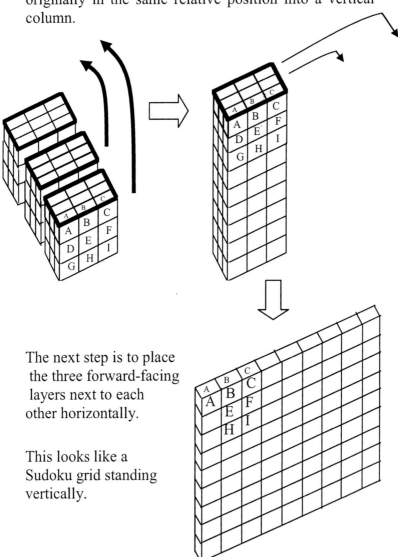

The next step is to place the three forward-facing layers next to each other horizontally.

This looks like a Sudoku grid standing vertically.

Then separate the grid into 3 x 9 rectangles and place them one in front of the other.

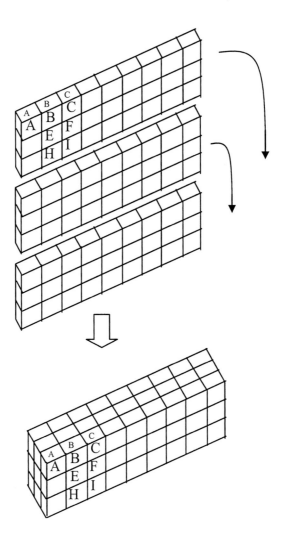

Finally separate this block into three 3 x 3 x 3 cubes. The left/right facing layers are the squares that are in the same relative positions in the original grid. **This view shows the cells of Rule Six of Hypercube Sudoku as nine cubes in the same layer.**

Notice the forward facing layers here are the rows in the original grid. In the original grid what are the horizontal layers now in this arrangement?

This is just one of the ways to view a hypercube. A three-dimensional cube can be viewed from its six different faces. There are many more ways to view a hypercube.

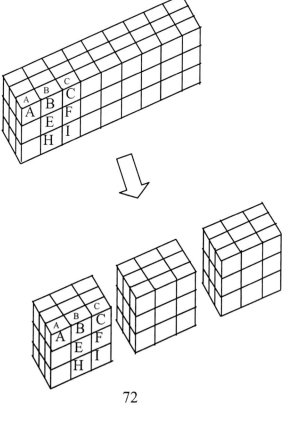

8. Hard Puzzles

		2						
			1					
							9	
	7					3		5
8	6							4

Puzzle **27** Hard

Puzzle **28** Hard

			9					
6			3		5	9		
8			1		7	4		
			7	1				

Puzzle **29** Hard

				9				
				8				
	3	2	5	7			8	1
				1				
				6				

Puzzle **30** Hard

1						3	7	
							2	
							4	
				5			6	
				8				

Puzzle **31** Hard

1			2			3		
								4
7			8					5
6			1			5		

Puzzle **32** Hard

	4							
								3
			7	5				
					2			
9								
8							6	7
		2		1				

Puzzle **33** Hard

7							9	
2	3		1		4		5	
				2				
			5		3			
1								6

Puzzle **34** Hard

			1	2	3			
			2			4		
			5			1		
						6		
				8	7			

Puzzle **35** Hard

			2		9			
			4					
			1	6				
						3		
			3	5	7			

Puzzle **36** Hard

82

	6						5	
						7		
		8						
		3		7				
	6				9			
4						1		

Puzzle **37** Hard

7	3		5					
9								
4				6				
2								
8	7	4						

Puzzle **38** Hard

			7	4	5			
		1				2		
			8					
		7				4		
			3		6			

Puzzle **39** Hard

			6	3	8			
		7				2		
	4						3	
		6				7		
			9		1			

Puzzle **40** Hard

9. The Seventh Rule of Hypercube Sudoku

The rules of Sudoku and Hypercube Sudoku are stated in a positive ways; certain groups of squares must contain all the numbers from 1 to 9. In practice while one is solving a puzzle these rules are often used in a negative way. Certain numbers are excluded from certain squares. If there is a 4 in a square in the top row, 4 cannot be in any of the other squares in that row. When eight numbers have been excluded from a certain square, then the ninth number must go there. Also if a number has been excluded from all but one square in a group of squares, a column for instance, then that number must go in the remaining square.

Standard Sudoku has three rules for excluding numbers from connected spaces. Hypercube Sudoku has six rules. However there is an implicit 'seventh rule' for excluding numbers from related squares. Perhaps you have noticed when trying a number in a certain place, unintended contradictions arise. Here we shall see why this is.

Consider the grid below. There is a 1 in the top left corner square. The x's denote the squares where 1 is excluded due to the six rules of Hypercube Sudoku. However logically there are several other squares from which 1 is excluded.

1	X	X	X	X	X	X	X	X
X	X	X	X			X		
X	X	X	X			X		
X	X	X	X			X		
X								
X								
X	X	X	X			X		
X								
X								

In the grid below there is a 1 in the top left corner square and x's denote the squares that this 1 prohibit other 1's to be placed. Another 1 is placed in the lower right corner and z 's denote the squares that this 1 prohibits.

Some squares have both x and z. This is not a problem. In those squares 1 is doubly prohibited. However, notice that in the upper right block and the lower left block only one square, the center square, has not been eliminated. This means that 1 must go in the center square of these two blocks, but this contradicts the sixth rule. If 1 is in the center of one block then it cannot go in the center of any other block.

1	X	X	X	X	X	X	X	X
X	X	X	X			X		Z
X	X	X	X		Z	X	Z	Z
X	X	X	X			X		Z
X								Z
X		Z			Z	Z	Z	Z
X	X	X	X		Z	X	Z	Z
X		Z			Z	Z	Z	Z
X	Z	Z	Z	Z	Z	Z	Z	1

Therefore if a number is in the upper left square of the grid, the same number cannot go in the lower right corner even though this does not directly contradict any of the six rules.

There are several other squares that are similarly excluded. These are shown in the grid below.

1								
				X	X		X	X
				X	X		X	X
				X	X		X	X
				X	X		X	X

Of course this type of exclusion holds for all positions, not just the upper left corner. This exclusion rule can be stated generally as follows, **The Seventh Rule of Hypercube Sudoku: for a number placed in any square, in the blocks not in the same row or column the squares containing that number must be in the same relative row or column as the original square.**

In the grid on the previous page the x's show the spaces in which a 1 cannot be placed due to this seventh exclusion rule if a 1 is placed in the upper right corner. Of course if the initial number is placed in a different square the excluded squares are different.

The following grids show a few other examples.

				1				
X	X					X	X	
X	X					X	X	
X	X					X	X	
X	X					X	X	

			X		X	X		X
			X		X	X		X
	1							
			X		X	X		X
			X		X	X		X

Notice this seventh exclusion rule deals only with squares in blocks that are not in the same row or column of the block of the initial square. The excluded squares in these blocks are in neither the same relative row or column of the block as the row and column of the initial square.

This seventh rule can be combined with the first six rules to make one generalized exclusion rule, **The General Exclusion Rule of Hypercube Sudoku: for a number placed in any square, the coordinates of all other squares containing that number must have exactly one coordinate the same as the first square.**

The grid below show the consequences of this rule for the case where a 1 is in the upper left cell.

1	X	X	X	X	X	X	X	X
X	X	X	X			X		
X	X	X	X			X		
X	X	X	X			X		
X				X	X		X	X
X				X	X		X	X
X	X	X	X			X		
X				X	X		X	X
X				X	X		X	X

In the grid above we see in the upper row of blocks, possible squares are, of course, not in the same row as the original number and also they are not in the same relative column within the block. The 1 is in the left column of its block. In the other blocks in that row of blocks the left columns is excluded.

Similarly, in the left column of blocks, the available squares are not in the column (left) or row (top) within the block as the original 1.

In the blocks that are not in the same row or column of blocks as the original number, the available spaces are either in the top row of the block, the same row as the original 1, or the left column of the block, but not both.

The grid below shows a detailed comparison of the coordinates of the upper left cell with all the other cells. The coordinates that are the same as the upper left cell are shaded. Only the cells with exactly one coordinate shaded can have the same number as the upper right cell.

(1, 3, 1. 3)	(1, 3, 2. 3)	(1, 3, 3. 3)	(2, 3, 1. 3)	(2, 3, 2. 3)	(2, 3, 3. 3)	(3, 3, 1. 3)	(3, 3, 2. 3)	(3, 3, 3. 3)
(1, 3, 1. 2)	(1, 3, 2. 2)	(1, 3, 3. 2)	(2, 3, 1. 2)	(2, 3, 2. 2)	(2, 3, 3. 2)	(3, 3, 1. 2)	(3, 3, 2. 2)	(3, 3, 3. 2)
(1, 3, 1. 1)	(1, 3, 2. 1)	(1, 3, 3. 1)	(2, 3, 1. 1)	(2, 3, 2. 1)	(2, 3, 3. 1)	(3, 3, 1. 1)	(3, 3, 2. 1)	(3, 3, 3. 1)
(1, 2, 1. 3)	(1, 2, 2. 3)	(1, 2, 3. 3)	(2, 2, 1. 3)	(2, 2, 2. 3)	(2, 2, 3. 3)	(3, 2, 1. 3)	(3, 2, 2. 3)	(3, 2, 3. 3)
(1, 2, 1. 2)	(1, 2, 2. 2)	(1, 2, 3. 2)	(2, 2, 1. 2)	(2, 2, 2. 2)	(2, 2, 3. 2)	(3, 2, 1. 2)	(3, 2, 2. 2)	(3, 2, 3. 2)
(1, 2, 1. 1)	(1, 2, 2. 1)	(1, 2, 3. 1)	(2, 2, 1. 1)	(2, 2, 2. 1)	(2, 2, 3. 1)	(3, 2, 1. 1)	(3, 2, 2. 1)	(3, 2, 3. 1)
(1, 1, 1. 3)	(1, 1, 2. 3)	(1, 1, 3. 3)	(2, 1, 1. 3)	(2, 1, 2. 3)	(2, 1, 3. 3)	(3, 1, 1. 3)	(3, 1, 2. 3)	(3, 1, 3. 3)
(1, 1, 1. 2)	(1, 1, 2. 2)	(1, 1, 3. 2)	(2, 1, 1. 2)	(2, 1, 2. 2)	(2, 1, 3. 2)	(3, 1, 1. 2)	(3, 1, 2. 2)	(3, 1, 3. 2)
(1, 1, 1. 1)	(1, 1, 2. 1)	(1, 1, 3. 1)	(2, 1, 1. 1)	(2, 1, 2. 1)	(2, 1, 3. 1)	(3, 1, 1. 1)	(3, 1, 2. 1)	(3, 1, 3. 1)

Another way to state the **General Exclusion Rule is: Like numbers in the same row or column of blocks must be in different rows and columns within their blocks. Like numbers not in the same row or column of blocks must be in the same row or column but not both within their blocks.**

The two grids on the previous two pages show the general rule with respect to only cell. The two following grids show the configuration with respect to two other cells.

	X		X		X	X		X
X	X	X						
	X		X		X	X		X
X	X	X		X			X	
X	1	X	X	X	X	X	X	X
X	X	X		X			X	
	X		X		X	X		X
X	X	X						
	X		X		X	X		X

		X	X	X	X			X
X	X	X	X	X	1	X	X	X
		X	X	X	X			X
X	X				X	X	X	
			X	X	X			
X	X				X	X	X	
X	X				X	X	X	
			X	X	X			
X	X				X	X	X	

The Seventh Rule might be a bit harder to use than the first six and it is not always needed to solve a puzzle. It is not needed for the easy and medium puzzles in this book. So try the first six rules first and only use the seventh rule when you get stuck.

10. Very Hard Puzzles

9					1			
						2		
	7							
8								
			3					
		6					7	
								4

Puzzle **41** Very Hard

			5		4			
	2		1	8	6		5	
				4			7	
				9				

Puzzle **42** Very Hard

7								
		4				2		
		6				3		
2				6				
		9						
					1	5		

Puzzle **43** Very Hard

					5	6		
	1							
			9					
	3				2			
						8		
4								

Puzzle **44** Very Hard

1								2
	7							
			9					
					5			
		8		4				
6								
						3		

Puzzle **45** Very Hard

					4			
7							1	
5								
				9				
	8		2					
								3

Puzzle **46** Very Hard

						5		
			8					
			4	7		1		
		2						3
	6	5						1
								4

Puzzle **47** Very Hard

3								9
			1				6	
			3					
	5	2						
7								
				4				

Puzzle **48** Very Hard

	8					4		
						1		
					5			
			9	7				
							2	
	6							

Puzzle **49** Very Hard

			7					
		9						
	1					3		
		5				4		
		6						
2								

Puzzle **50** Very Hard

11. Solutions

6	7	1	3	2	4	9	5	8
2	4	3	5	8	9	1	6	7
8	9	5	7	1	6	4	3	2
5	8	9	1	6	7	2	4	3
7	1	6	4	3	2	8	9	5
3	2	4	9	5	8	6	7	1
4	3	2	8	9	5	7	1	6
9	5	8	6	7	1	3	2	4
1	6	7	2	4	3	5	8	9

Puzzle 1

2	8	3	5	4	7	1	9	6
7	6	4	8	1	9	3	2	5
9	5	1	6	3	2	4	7	8
6	1	9	3	2	8	7	5	4
5	3	2	4	7	6	9	8	1
8	4	7	1	9	5	2	6	3
4	7	5	9	6	1	8	3	2
1	9	8	2	5	3	6	4	7
3	2	6	7	8	4	5	1	9

Puzzle 2

107

4	5	3	7	6	9	1	2	8
9	7	2	8	1	5	3	4	6
6	8	1	2	3	4	5	9	7
2	9	7	5	8	1	6	3	4
1	6	8	4	2	3	7	5	9
3	4	5	9	7	6	8	1	2
8	1	6	3	4	2	9	7	5
5	3	4	6	9	7	2	8	1
7	2	9	1	5	8	4	6	3

Puzzle 3

2	4	9	7	6	8	1	3	5
8	5	1	4	9	3	6	2	7
3	7	6	5	1	2	9	8	4
6	8	7	3	5	1	4	9	2
9	3	4	2	7	6	5	1	8
1	2	5	8	4	9	7	6	3
5	1	3	9	2	4	8	7	6
7	6	2	1	8	5	3	4	9
4	9	8	6	3	7	2	5	1

Puzzle 4

8	4	7	1	6	5	9	2	3
2	5	1	4	3	9	6	7	8
3	9	6	7	8	2	5	1	4
5	1	2	3	9	4	7	8	6
9	6	3	8	2	7	1	4	5
4	7	8	6	5	1	2	3	9
6	3	9	2	7	8	4	5	1
7	8	4	5	1	6	3	9	2
1	2	5	9	4	3	8	6	7

Puzzle 5

Puzzle 6

8	9	2	4	6	7	3	1	5
7	3	1	5	8	9	2	4	6
6	5	4	1	2	3	9	7	8
5	4	6	2	3	1	7	8	9
9	2	8	6	7	4	1	5	3
3	1	7	8	9	5	4	6	2
1	7	3	9	5	8	6	2	4
4	6	5	3	1	2	8	9	7
2	8	9	7	4	6	5	3	1

Puzzle 7

3	2	4	9	5	7	1	6	8
7	9	5	8	1	6	4	3	2
6	8	1	2	4	3	5	7	9
5	1	9	6	8	2	7	4	3
2	6	8	3	7	4	9	5	1
4	3	7	1	9	5	8	2	6
8	7	6	4	3	1	2	9	5
1	4	3	5	2	9	6	8	7
9	5	2	7	6	8	3	1	4

Puzzle 8

4	7	1	8	9	2	3	5	6
5	6	3	1	4	7	2	8	9
9	2	8	6	3	5	7	1	4
6	3	5	7	1	4	9	2	8
8	9	2	3	5	6	4	7	1
1	4	7	2	8	9	5	6	3
2	8	9	5	6	3	1	4	7
7	1	4	9	2	8	6	3	5
3	5	6	4	7	1	8	9	2

Puzzle 9

2	8	4	6	7	9	3	1	5
1	6	7	5	3	2	4	9	8
9	5	3	8	4	1	7	2	6
5	3	1	4	2	8	9	6	7
8	4	9	7	1	6	2	5	3
6	7	2	3	9	5	1	8	4
7	9	6	1	5	3	8	4	2
3	2	5	9	8	4	6	7	1
4	1	8	2	6	7	5	3	9

Puzzle 9

Puzzle 10

5	7	4	1	2	6	3	8	9
9	3	8	4	5	7	2	6	1
6	1	2	8	9	3	7	4	5
8	9	3	7	4	5	6	1	2
1	2	6	3	8	9	5	7	4
4	5	7	2	6	1	9	3	8
2	6	1	9	3	8	4	5	7
7	4	5	6	1	2	8	9	3
3	8	9	5	7	4	1	2	6

Puzzle 10

Puzzle 11

2	7	6	8	1	3	9	4	5
4	8	1	5	9	2	6	3	7
3	5	9	7	6	4	1	2	8
1	3	8	4	5	9	7	6	2
9	2	5	3	7	6	8	1	4
6	4	7	2	8	1	5	9	3
5	9	4	6	2	7	3	8	1
7	6	3	1	4	8	2	5	9
8	1	2	9	3	5	4	7	6

Puzzle 11

Puzzle 12

3	1	7	8	4	6	9	2	5
6	8	4	5	9	2	1	7	3
2	5	9	7	3	1	4	6	8
4	6	8	2	5	9	7	3	1
9	2	5	3	1	7	8	4	6
1	7	3	6	8	4	5	9	2
5	9	2	1	7	3	6	8	4
7	3	1	4	6	8	2	5	9
8	4	6	9	2	5	3	1	7

Puzzle 13

7	9	8	4	1	2	6	3	5
3	5	6	9	8	7	2	4	1
1	2	4	5	6	3	8	7	9
5	6	3	8	7	9	1	2	4
4	1	2	6	3	5	7	9	8
9	8	7	2	4	1	3	5	6
2	4	1	3	5	6	9	8	7
8	7	9	1	2	4	5	6	3
6	3	5	7	9	8	4	1	2

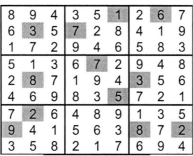

Puzzle 14

8	9	4	3	5	1	2	6	7
6	3	5	7	2	8	4	1	9
1	7	2	9	4	6	5	8	3
5	1	3	6	7	2	9	4	8
2	8	7	1	9	4	3	5	6
4	6	9	8	3	5	7	2	1
7	2	6	4	8	9	1	3	5
9	4	1	5	6	3	8	7	2
3	5	8	2	1	7	6	9	4

Puzzle15

9	7	3	2	1	4	6	8	5
5	6	8	3	9	7	4	2	1
1	4	2	8	5	6	7	3	9
8	2	1	5	6	9	3	4	7
7	3	4	1	8	2	9	5	6
6	9	5	4	7	3	2	1	8
4	5	6	7	3	8	1	9	2
2	1	9	6	4	5	8	7	3
3	8	7	9	2	1	5	6	4

Puzzle 16

8	4	7	3	6	2	9	5	1
5	1	9	7	8	4	2	3	6
6	2	3	1	9	5	4	7	8
1	9	5	4	7	8	6	2	3
3	6	2	9	5	1	8	4	7
7	8	4	2	3	6	5	1	9
2	3	6	5	1	9	7	8	4
4	7	8	6	2	3	1	9	5
9	5	1	8	4	7	3	6	2

Puzzle 17

8	6	7	4	3	1	2	9	5
1	5	3	6	2	9	7	8	4
9	4	2	5	7	8	3	1	6
5	2	9	7	8	6	1	4	3
4	7	8	3	1	5	9	6	2
6	3	1	2	9	4	8	5	7
3	1	4	9	5	2	6	7	8
2	9	6	8	4	7	5	3	1
7	8	5	1	6	3	4	2	9

Puzzle 18

6	8	3	2	5	9	7	1	4
1	4	7	8	3	6	5	9	2
9	2	5	4	7	1	3	6	8
4	9	1	3	6	7	8	2	5
2	5	8	9	1	4	6	7	3
7	3	6	5	8	2	1	4	9
5	7	2	1	4	8	9	3	6
3	6	9	7	2	5	4	8	1
8	1	4	6	9	3	2	5	7

Puzzle 19

8	5	3	6	9	2	4	1	7
2	6	9	1	7	4	5	3	8
7	4	1	3	8	5	9	2	6
9	2	6	7	4	1	3	8	5
4	1	7	8	5	3	6	9	2
5	3	8	2	6	9	1	7	4
1	7	4	5	3	8	2	6	9
3	8	5	9	2	6	7	4	1
6	9	2	4	1	7	8	5	3

Puzzle 20

5	8	7	1	9	4	2	3	6
9	4	1	6	2	3	7	5	8
3	6	2	8	7	5	4	1	9
4	1	9	3	6	2	8	7	5
2	3	6	5	8	7	1	9	4
7	5	8	9	4	1	6	2	3
6	2	3	7	5	8	9	4	1
8	7	5	4	1	9	3	6	2
1	9	4	2	3	6	5	8	7

Puzzle 21

3	2	8	5	4	6	7	1	9
1	9	7	8	3	2	6	5	4
4	6	5	9	7	1	2	8	3
9	7	1	2	8	3	4	6	5
5	4	6	7	1	9	3	2	8
8	3	2	6	5	4	1	9	7
6	5	4	1	9	7	8	3	2
2	8	3	4	6	5	9	7	1
7	1	9	3	2	8	5	4	6

Puzzle 22

2	3	4	8	5	7	9	1	6
6	9	8	1	2	3	7	4	5
5	7	1	4	6	9	3	8	2
1	6	9	3	4	2	5	7	8
4	5	7	9	8	6	2	3	1
8	2	3	7	1	5	6	9	4
7	8	5	6	9	1	4	2	3
3	1	2	5	7	4	8	6	9
9	4	6	2	3	8	1	5	7

Puzzle 23

7	1	4	9	8	5	2	6	3
8	5	9	6	3	2	1	4	7
3	2	6	4	7	1	5	9	8
6	9	8	3	2	7	4	5	1
2	7	3	5	1	4	9	8	6
1	4	5	8	6	9	7	3	2
5	3	2	1	4	6	8	7	9
4	6	1	7	9	8	3	2	5
9	8	7	2	5	3	6	1	4

```
5 7 1 | 4 3 8 | 2 6 9
8 4 2 | 9 1 6 | 3 5 7
6 9 3 | 7 2 5 | 1 8 4
------+-------+------
9 2 6 | 1 5 7 | 8 4 3
7 3 5 | 2 8 4 | 6 9 1
4 1 8 | 3 6 9 | 5 7 2
------+-------+------
3 8 4 | 6 9 2 | 7 1 5
1 6 9 | 5 7 3 | 4 2 8
2 5 7 | 8 4 1 | 9 3 6
```

Puzzle 24

```
2 3 1 | 6 7 4 | 8 9 5
9 5 8 | 3 1 2 | 7 4 6
4 6 7 | 5 8 9 | 1 2 3
------+-------+------
7 8 6 | 9 5 3 | 4 1 2
1 2 4 | 8 6 7 | 5 3 9
3 9 5 | 2 4 1 | 6 7 8
------+-------+------
5 4 9 | 1 2 8 | 3 6 7
6 7 3 | 4 9 5 | 2 8 1
8 1 2 | 7 3 6 | 9 5 4
```

Puzzle 25

```
5 8 7 | 9 3 6 | 2 4 1
6 9 3 | 1 2 4 | 7 5 8
4 1 2 | 8 7 5 | 3 6 9
------+-------+------
3 6 4 | 7 1 2 | 8 9 5
2 7 1 | 5 8 9 | 4 3 6
9 5 8 | 6 4 3 | 1 2 7
------+-------+------
1 2 9 | 4 5 8 | 6 7 3
8 4 5 | 3 6 7 | 9 1 2
7 3 6 | 2 9 1 | 5 8 4
```

Puzzle 26

Puzzle 27

9	1	2	5	3	4	8	6	7
7	8	6	1	2	9	4	5	3
3	4	5	6	7	8	2	9	1
6	7	8	2	9	1	3	4	5
5	3	4	8	6	7	9	1	2
1	2	9	4	5	3	7	8	6
4	5	3	7	8	6	1	2	9
2	9	1	3	4	5	6	7	8
8	6	7	9	1	2	5	3	4

Puzzle 27

Puzzle 28

5	7	2	8	3	1	6	9	4
3	6	8	9	4	7	1	2	5
4	1	9	2	5	6	7	8	3
9	4	6	7	2	5	3	1	8
2	5	1	6	8	3	4	7	9
8	3	7	1	9	4	5	6	2
1	8	3	4	6	9	2	5	7
7	9	4	5	1	2	8	3	6
6	2	5	3	7	8	9	4	1

Puzzle 28

Puzzle 29

4	5	3	8	9	2	1	6	7
7	1	6	5	3	4	2	8	9
9	2	8	6	7	1	3	4	5
6	7	1	3	4	5	9	2	8
8	9	2	1	6	7	4	5	3
5	3	4	2	8	9	7	1	6
2	8	9	7	1	6	5	3	4
3	4	5	9	2	8	6	7	1
1	6	7	4	5	3	8	9	2

Puzzle 29

116

Puzzle 30

1	4	8	2	9	3	7	6	5
5	7	6	4	8	1	9	3	2
3	2	9	6	5	7	8	1	4
9	3	2	5	7	6	4	8	1
8	1	4	3	2	9	6	5	7
7	6	5	1	4	8	2	9	3
6	5	7	8	1	4	3	2	9
2	9	3	7	6	5	1	4	8
4	8	1	9	3	2	5	7	6

Puzzle 30

Puzzle 31

1	8	5	2	9	6	3	7	4
7	6	3	8	4	1	9	5	2
4	2	9	5	3	7	6	1	8
6	3	7	4	1	8	5	2	9
2	9	4	3	7	5	1	8	6
8	5	1	9	6	2	7	4	3
9	4	2	7	5	3	8	6	1
5	1	8	6	2	9	4	3	7
3	7	6	1	8	4	2	9	5

Puzzle 31

Puzzle 32

1	6	7	2	4	8	3	5	9
5	9	3	6	7	1	4	8	2
8	2	4	9	3	5	7	1	6
9	8	2	5	1	3	6	7	4
7	4	6	8	2	9	1	3	5
3	5	1	4	6	7	2	9	8
4	3	5	7	9	6	8	2	1
2	1	8	3	5	4	9	6	7
6	7	9	1	8	2	5	4	3

Puzzle 32

Puzzle 33

2	4	8	9	3	1	6	7	5
5	6	7	8	2	4	1	9	3
3	1	9	7	5	6	4	8	2
7	5	6	4	8	2	3	1	9
9	3	1	6	7	5	2	4	8
8	2	4	1	9	3	5	6	7
1	9	3	5	6	7	8	2	4
4	8	2	3	1	9	7	5	6
6	7	5	2	4	8	9	3	1

Puzzle 33

Puzzle 34

4	1	8	9	7	5	6	2	3
7	6	2	8	3	1	5	9	4
3	5	9	2	4	6	1	8	7
2	3	6	1	8	4	7	5	9
9	4	5	6	2	7	3	1	8
8	7	1	5	9	3	4	6	2
5	9	7	3	6	2	8	4	1
1	8	3	4	5	9	2	7	6
6	2	4	7	1	8	9	3	5

Puzzle 34

Puzzle 35

7	9	2	6	5	4	3	1	8
4	3	1	8	7	9	2	6	5
5	8	6	1	2	3	9	4	7
8	6	5	2	3	1	4	7	9
9	2	7	5	4	6	1	8	3
3	1	4	7	9	8	6	5	2
1	4	3	9	8	7	5	2	6
6	5	8	3	1	2	7	9	4
2	7	9	4	6	5	8	3	1

Puzzle 35

7	4	5	8	1	6	9	2	3
3	9	2	5	7	4	6	8	1
1	6	8	2	3	9	4	5	7
6	3	1	4	9	2	5	7	8
8	5	7	1	6	3	2	4	9
9	2	4	7	8	5	3	1	6
2	8	9	3	5	7	1	6	4
4	1	6	9	2	8	7	3	5
5	7	3	6	4	1	8	9	2

Puzzle 36

5	9	8	6	7	2	3	4	1
2	6	7	1	3	4	8	5	9
4	1	3	9	8	5	7	2	6
7	3	4	8	1	9	2	6	5
9	8	1	5	2	6	4	7	3
6	5	2	3	4	7	1	9	8
1	2	6	4	5	3	9	8	7
3	4	5	7	9	8	6	1	2
8	7	9	2	6	1	5	3	4

Puzzle 37

7	3	8	5	2	4	6	9	1
9	1	6	3	8	7	2	4	5
4	5	2	1	6	9	8	7	3
2	6	5	9	1	3	4	8	7
8	7	4	6	5	2	1	3	9
3	9	1	7	4	8	5	2	6
1	4	9	8	7	6	3	5	2
5	2	3	4	9	1	7	6	8
6	8	7	2	3	5	9	1	4

Puzzle 38

Puzzle 39

4	5	3	8	2	9	1	6	7
2	7	8	6	3	1	5	9	4
9	1	6	7	4	5	3	8	2
6	9	1	5	7	4	2	3	8
3	4	5	9	8	2	7	1	6
8	2	7	1	6	3	4	5	9
7	8	2	3	1	6	9	4	5
1	6	9	4	5	7	8	2	3
5	3	4	2	9	8	6	7	1

Puzzle 39

Puzzle 40

4	8	9	7	2	5	3	1	6
2	6	3	1	9	4	8	5	7
5	7	1	6	3	8	9	4	2
1	5	7	8	6	3	2	9	4
9	4	8	5	7	2	6	3	1
3	2	6	4	1	9	7	8	5
6	3	2	9	4	1	5	7	8
7	1	5	3	8	6	4	2	9
8	9	4	2	5	7	1	6	3

Puzzle 40

Puzzle 41

9	2	4	5	3	1	7	8	6
3	1	5	8	6	7	2	4	9
6	7	8	4	9	2	1	5	3
8	6	3	2	7	9	4	1	5
7	9	2	1	5	4	6	3	8
5	4	1	3	8	6	9	2	7
1	5	7	6	4	8	3	9	2
4	8	6	9	2	3	5	7	1
2	3	9	7	1	5	8	6	4

Puzzle 41

Puzzle 42

9	6	1	5	7	4	2	3	8
4	5	7	8	2	3	1	9	6
3	8	2	6	1	9	7	4	5
7	2	3	1	8	6	4	5	9
6	1	8	9	4	5	3	7	2
5	9	4	2	3	7	8	6	1
8	4	5	3	9	2	6	1	7
2	3	9	7	6	1	5	8	4
1	7	6	4	5	8	9	2	3

Puzzle 42

Puzzle 43

7	5	2	6	4	3	1	8	9
8	9	1	5	2	7	4	3	6
3	6	4	9	1	8	2	7	5
4	1	6	8	9	5	3	2	7
2	7	3	1	6	4	9	5	8
5	8	9	7	3	2	6	4	1
9	3	8	2	7	1	5	6	4
6	4	5	3	8	9	7	1	2
1	2	7	4	5	6	8	9	3

Puzzle 43

Puzzle 44

3	4	8	1	2	5	6	9	7
9	5	6	4	7	3	2	8	1
7	1	2	8	6	9	5	3	4
2	7	1	9	8	6	4	5	3
8	3	4	5	1	2	7	6	9
6	9	5	3	4	7	1	2	8
5	6	9	7	3	4	8	1	2
1	2	7	6	9	8	3	4	5
4	8	3	2	5	1	9	7	6

Puzzle 44

Puzzle 45

1	8	9	3	5	6	7	4	2
5	7	3	4	2	8	6	9	1
2	6	4	9	1	7	8	3	5
4	2	7	8	9	1	5	6	3
9	1	6	7	3	5	2	8	4
3	5	8	6	4	2	1	7	9
6	3	5	2	7	4	9	1	8
8	4	2	1	6	9	3	5	7
7	9	1	5	8	3	4	2	6

Puzzle 45

Puzzle 46

2	9	5	1	8	4	3	6	7
6	4	1	9	7	3	8	5	2
7	3	8	5	2	6	4	1	9
8	7	3	6	5	2	9	4	1
5	2	9	4	1	8	7	3	6
1	6	4	3	9	7	2	8	5
4	1	6	7	3	9	5	2	8
3	8	7	2	6	5	1	9	4
9	5	2	8	4	1	6	7	3

Puzzle 46

Puzzle 47

7	3	4	2	1	9	5	8	6
9	2	1	8	6	5	3	4	7
6	5	8	4	7	3	1	9	2
1	9	2	6	5	8	4	7	3
5	8	6	7	3	4	2	1	9
3	4	7	9	2	1	8	6	5
8	6	5	3	4	7	9	2	1
4	7	3	1	9	2	6	5	8
2	1	9	5	8	6	7	3	4

Puzzle 47

122